ORCHIDS O

— even Solomon in all his glory was not arrayed like one of these. St. Matthew 6:29

ORCHIDS OF GREECE

WITH A FOREWORD BY
MARY BRIGGS F.P.S., F.L.S.
Honorary General Secretary, The Botanical
Society of the British Isles

J.D. Lepper

ARTHUR H. STOCKWELL LTD.
Elms Court   Ilfracombe
Devon

To
MY MOTHER

ISBN 0 7223 1450-7

Printed in Great Britain by
Arthur H. Stockwell Ltd.
Elms Court   Ilfracombe
Devon

Contents

Illustrations
Set between pp. 32 & 33

4 *Serapias parviflora* (two-thirds size)
5 *Serapias vomeracea* (two-thirds size)
6 Flower of *Serapias vomeracea* (one and two-thirds size)

Plate VIII
1 *Aceras anthropophorum* (two-thirds size)
2 *Anacamptis pyramidalis ssp. brachystachys* (two-thirds size)
3 *Barlia robertiana* (one-third size)
4 *Cephalanthera ensifolia* (one-third size)
5 *Limodorum abortivum* (size)
6 *Neotinea maculata* (one and two-thirds size)

Foreword

This book will add greatly to the pleasure of all flower lovers taking their holidays in Greece or on the Aegean Islands, by helping them to sort out, identify and perhaps to look more closely at, the wild orchids. These are certainly among the most spectacular of all the wild plants of this very rich area. For those fortunate travellers who have already visited this lovely corner of the world and have seen the orchids, this book will bring back many happy memories.

I have had the pleasure of taking the author on botanical tours, when his keen enthusiasm for, and his knowledge of, the orchids that we found were shared generously with all the members of the parties — as they are in this book. Desmond's enthusiasm for his subject shines through his text, and together with the fine photographic illustrations (for which much labour was expended to achieve the perfection that he sought) I commend the book to be enjoyed by flower lovers, Hellenophiles and orchidologists.

MARY BRIGGS

October 1980   Slinfold, Sussex

Preface

People are often impressed by orchids. The popular image of steaming jungles and exotic flowers suggests an air of mystery and romance. Thanks largely to the intrepid collectors who introduced them, there are today some 25,000 orchid species known to science. These include a number of plants which flourish in temperate climates. The orchids of the temperate zone, although smaller than many of their tropical relations, are nevertheless just as beautiful in their own way. Amongst them are some 49 species native to the British Isles. The orchids of Greece include a number of the British species, and their flowers are usually larger and more richly coloured than those found in Britain.

The amateur plant lover is sometimes heard to complain of the use of botanical Latin names. This practice has the great advantage of stamping the plant with a name which can be recognised throughout the world.

But perhaps the amateur can be forgiven for complaining of the tendency to change these names from time to time. Those readers who are already familiar with Greek orchids will, I hope, bear with me when finding that a plant which is known to them by one name has been given a different one. The substitution has been made in order to conform with the most recent classification of orchids. Where there are synonyms, I have used them.

J.D.L.
Dalwood, 1980

Acknowledgements

I should like to record my grateful thanks to Axminster Duplicating Service for their patient work in the typing of the manuscript.

I should also like to express my warmest thanks to Mr P.F. Hunt, formerly of The Herbarium, The Royal Botanic Gardens, Kew, for his most helpful criticisms and suggestions.

Lastly, but certainly not least, I should like to record my most sincere gratitude to Mrs Mary Briggs, Honorary General Secretary of The Botanical Society of the British Isles, for her kindness in writing the Foreword to this book.

Chapter I

THE STRUCTURE OF THE ORCHID FLOWER

The natural order Orchidaceae is one of the largest plant families on earth, and its flowers exhibit more variation in colour, shape and size than those of any other. The flowers are nearly all hermaphrodite, that is to say, each contains both male and female organs; and they need the help of a pollinating insect in order to achieve fertilisation leading to seed production. The great naturalist Charles Darwin, in his book *The Various Contrivances by which Orchids are Fertilised by Insects*, describes the extraordinary methods by which pollination of the flowers is effected.

Orchids are believed to have evolved from lilies; broadly speaking, the flowers of the lily and the orchid show some botanical similarity. But there are two essential differences by which the orchid can always be distinguished, namely, the organs known as the lip, or labellum, and the column. Whereas the flowers of the lily possess three sepals and three petals (the outer and inner whorls respectively) those of the orchid possess three sepals, two petals and the lip, the latter being a modified third petal. The flower of the lily possesses individual stamens and pistil (the male and female organs respectively), while that of the orchid combines both organs in the column; the two pollen masses, or pollinia, are located at the tip of the column, and the stigmatic surface, equivalent to the pistil, towards its base.

The lip nearly always differs in shape, size or colour from the other parts of the orchid flower. It is thus made to stand out, and provides a conspicuous 'landing ground' for the visiting insect, who travels up its length to its base beneath the overhanging column in search of nectar. On backing out, the insect operates a 'trigger' mechanism, causing the pollinia, which are joined at their base by a sticky disc, to adhere to its head. And here is a significant fact. When first withdrawn, the pollinia stand up at right angles to the insect's body. During the course of a few seconds, however, the sticky disc contracts, making the pollinia move forward through an angle of ninety degrees until they are pointing straight forward. On the insect entering the next flower visited, they at once come into contact with the stigmatic surface. This clever arrangement ensures that cross pollination takes place, and not self-pollination of a flower with its own pollen.

Another interesting feature of the lip lies in the fact that in the immature bud it lies uppermost. During the bud's development, the stalk of each flower (which is known as the pedicel and which later on forms the seed capsule) twists through an angle of one hundred and eighty degrees, so that by the time the flower opens the lip is pointing downwards, and is ready to receive the landing insect.

In some orchids, notably the temperate Ophrys species, the flower resembles the female of the pollinating insect, and the male is attracted sexually.

In attempting to mate, he pollinates the flower. It also happens that the males of most species of pollinating insect emerge a fortnight or so before the females, so that they are at first exclusively attracted by the orchid flowers, thus ensuring fertilisation.

The insects do not always confine themselves to orchids of the same species, but collect pollen from the flower of one species, and deposit it on that of another. This leads to the formation of hybrid plants, making identification in the field very difficult, although it adds interest to the study of the plants. Familiarity with the flowers and an eye for botanical detail, coupled with an understanding of the parts of the orchid flower, will make this task a little easier. Some remarkable natural hybrids have been recorded as a result of this random cross fertilisation.

Orchids belong to the group of plants known as monocotyledons, that is to say, plants bearing a single seed-leaf. Their leaves vary in shape and length, but in common with other plants of this group, the leaf veins are parallel and not branched. The underground parts of the plants generally consist of two or three roughly ovoid tubers, whose shapes vary from one species to another. From these grow the young shoots which eventually produce the flower spikes.

Chapter II

THE HAUNTS OF GREEK ORCHIDS

The modern tourist is no stranger to Greece. Holiday brochures in every travel agent's window, and the heavy bookings which result from them, testify to her popularity. Two of her main attractions are her climate and her antiquities; but there is a third which, although well known, is not perhaps so widely enjoyed, and that is her flora. Amongst the plants whose flowers carpet the ground in places during spring and early summer are some 50 orchid species, most of them spring flowering. For the purpose of describing some of their habitats it is perhaps convenient to divide the country into five areas: namely, the mainland, the Aegean Islands, Corfu, Rhodes and Crete.

THE MAINLAND

Athens, as the capital of Greece, needs no introductions, with its famous landmarks such as the Parthenon and St Paul's Rock. From the city, an excellent coach service caters for the tourist and covers the various areas of the country.

As might be expected, the Greek mainland holds the majority of the orchids of Greece. On the hills of open 'maquis' Ophrys and Serapias species occur, often accompanied by the small purple spikes of *Orchis quadripunctata*. Amongst the Ophrys the beautiful *O. speculum* must be singled out for special mention. Some magnificent forms can be found, with a large central lip patch of vivid blue. *Ophrys fusca* and its varieties are common, as is also *O. lutea*.

Many areas in the Peloponnese contain a number of Ophrys species, including *O. argolica* and *O. ferrum-equinum*. In some localities colonies of mixed species occur, resulting in hybrids which tax the expertise of the enthusiast. Amongst Orchis species the striking *O. italica* stands out, its large spikes of deep pink flowers often visible some distance away. Not perhaps so easily spotted will be *Aceras anthropophorum*, the Man orchid.

Much of the country is devoted to olive production, and the olive groves will be found to contain a wide variety of orchids. *Orchis papilionacea* and *O. provincialis* are two notable plants to be looked for in this type of habitat, as are also *O. pauciflora* and *Barlia robertiana*, the Giant orchid. Ophrys species will be well represented, notably *O. sphegodes* and its varieties, *O fusca* and *O. lutea*.

A search of open oak or pine scrub could well be rewarded with a sighting of the rather local *Limodorum abortivum*. In the mountainous areas species to be looked for include *Orchis anatolica* and the small *Neotinea maculata*. Here too occur the woodland-loving species of Cephalanthera and Epipactis, and while the spring visitor will be too early to see them in flower, a careful search could reveal well developed leaves and perhaps a young spike developing.

THE AEGEAN ISLANDS

The Aegean Sea, separating the east coast of Greece from the west coast of Turkey, contains a host of small islands which are much sought after by summer tourists seeking sun and sea air. It is not easy to cover the islands botanically in the course of a short visit, due to the problem of transport and the distances involved. A steamer service runs between the larger islands, but it is not very frequent until Easter, when the main tourist season normally opens; and in order to cover the area earlier than this, it is necessary to hire a boat.

Amongst the most well-known islands are Andros, Skyros, Naxos and Mykonos. The last named is perhaps one of the most popular. It is a small island, some ten miles across from east to west, and it lies in a south-easterly direction from Athens, being roughly equidistant from Greece and Turkey.

The harbour at Mykonos is typical of the Greek islands, the sea front giving way to narrow streets winding between white houses. On the open hillsides, *Serapias cordigera* can be found, together with *Ophrys sphegodes*. The pretty blue *Iris sisyrinchium* is widespread.

Just off the south-western tip of the island lies Delos, a smaller island but archaeologically very interesting. Despite its rather scanty water supply Delos, which is uninhabited, is noted for its spring flowers. It is easily reached by boat from Mykonos.

The islands of Samos, Naxos and Karpathos are especially interesting botanically, the two last named yielding the beautiful *Ophrys cretica* which, apart from Crete itself, is found nowhere else.

CORFU

Corfu, the largest of the Ionian Islands, lies just off the north-western tip of Greece which borders Albania. The capital, Corfu City, is situated roughly midway down the east coast. The island is particularly noted for its olive trees, some of which are hundreds of years old. Due to its high rainfall, Corfu is extremely fertile, and its flora is a particularly rich one; this is borne out by its orchid flora, which rivals that of Crete. The island is also of considerable interest to the ornithologist, being on the route of migrating birds.

The open 'maquis' in Corfu is rich in Ophrys species. Some fine forms of *O. scolopax var. cornuta* occur, together with *O. ferrum-equinum*, *O. sphegodes* and *O. tenthredinifera*. Other species of note include *Orchis simia*, *O. provincialis*, *O. italica* and *Aceras anthropophorum*. In patches of open woodland *Limodorum abortivum* may well be found, while in grassy areas both *Orchis coriophora* and *O. papilionacea* occur.

Many Serapias occur on the island, and they include *S. neglecta var. ionica* and *S. vomeracea*. Several species, notably *S. lingua* and *S. parviflora*, occur in mixed colonies, and this has led to extensive inter-hybridisation, making the identification of individuals difficult.

Where orchids occur in Corfu, they are often plentiful. In one location, a small hillside, the author has recorded nine species growing in close proximity to each other; amongst them are *Ophrys scolopax var. cornuta*, *O. ferrum-equinum* and *Orchis italica*. Throughout the island there are stands of the deep purple *Orchis laxiflora*, some specimens reaching a height of two feet or more, especially those growing in the long grass of marshy meadows.

RHODES

This island, famous for its links with the Crusaders, lies just south of the mainland of Turkey. The ancient city of Rhodes is situated at its northern tip. Roughly oval in shape, and some 20 miles from north to south, Rhodes is a fertile island, and its flora, which includes a white paeony peculiar to it, is a rich one.

The orchid hunter visiting Rhodes can expect to see a satisfying number of species. In woodland country such plants as *Orchis anatolica*, *O. lactea* and *O. pauciflora* will be found, while in the areas of open scrub Ophrys species occur, notably *O. speculum*, *O. sphegodes var. mammosa*, *O. fuciflora* and *O. scolopax var. heldreichii*. In the open grassy areas there are some good forms of *Orchis saccata*, while in the mountainous areas careful searching could reveal the small *Neotinea maculata*.

The town of Lindos, on the island's east coast is historically interesting, and the surrounding country is well worth exploring botanically. For those interested in scenery, the Valley of the Butterflies, which in mid-summer becomes the home of myriads of red-winged butterflies, is well worth a visit.

CRETE

Crete, perhaps the loveliest of all the Greek islands, lies well to the south of the mainland of Greece. It is, in fact, nearer to the Equator than the North African coast; consequently, spring comes early, and in order to see the wealth of spring flowers at their best, it is necessary to pay a visit during the period from mid-March to mid-April. The island is some 150 miles long from east to west, and some 35 miles across at its widest point. The capital, Heraklion, lies roughly midway along the north coast.

The orchid flora of Crete is as rich as that of any area of its size in the Mediterranean region. The eastern half of the island, from Heraklion to the eastern tip at Vai, has, if anything, a slightly drier climate than the western half. Chania in the west, Heraklion and Sitia in the east are all good centres on the north coast from which to explore the countryside southwards.

The classical sites, if not cleared of vegetation, provide excellent habitats for plants, as they are not grazed by the local farmers.

Much of the island consists of low hills of typical Greek 'maquis', always good orchid country. Amongst the large number of species which occur here are some excellent forms of *Ophrys fuciflora forma maxima*. This magnificent orchid, larger than its British counterpart, produces some outstanding forms with beautifully marked lips; in some specimens a 'horn' projects forwards from each side of the base of the lip.

In Crete, as in Corfu, orchids are often locally abundant, and the orchid hunter intent on plant photography would be well advised to take an ample supply of film.

Chapter III

HINTS ON ORCHID-HUNTING

Weather and Season

Plant-hunting is an enthralling pastime, and perhaps never more so than when the quarry is an orchid. It is obvious that weather and season play an important part in success or failure. The weather in Greece during March and April, the main flowering season for the orchids, is often a mixture of wet and dry conditions. Rain, although sometimes heavy, is usually short-lived and followed by clear weather, but the higher the altitude the later the warmer conditions, and consequently the later the flowering period. Much also depends on the earliness or lateness of a particular season, and advance notice of this can be very helpful when planning a visit. It is also important to realise that from Corfu, off the north-west coast, to Crete, well south of the mainland, is a considerable distance, and that the further south one goes the earlier the season. The following table gives a rough guide to the periods during which orchids could be seen at their best during an average season:

Crete	mid-March to mid-April
Rhodes	late March to late April
The Mainland and Islands	the month of April
Corfu	the month of April

All botanising is, of course, a mixture of triumphs and disappointments, but given an average season, the visitor to the above areas of Greece during the periods shown will be unlucky not to see at least a fair proportion of the species which they contain.

Likely Habitats

Experience in looking for orchids develops the ability to recognise a piece of ground where they are likely to occur. Generally speaking, thick and rank vegetation can be ignored. The plants prefer fairly short grass, or open clearings in woods where an adequate amount of light is available. Grassy banks below sloping woods are a favourite spot.

The coastal areas of Greece which have not been developed sometimes contain a number of species, notably Serapias and Ophrys, the latter occasionally frequenting sand-dunes. A fair proportion of the undeveloped areas is cultivated, but there is still a good deal of ground untouched, such as the southern tip of Corfu at Lefkimi and parts of the eastern end of Crete.

In many parts of Greece, particularly in Corfu, olives are grown, and the olive groves will often be found to yield a considerable number of species. Amongst the Ophrys could be *O. lutea*, *O. fusca*, *O. tenthredinifera* and *O. bombyliflora*. Likely Orchis species include *O. italica*, *O. provincialis*, *O. papilionacea* and *O. saccata*. The Giant orchid, *B. robertiana*, and the Man orchid, *A. anthropophorum* could also occur here.

Much of Greece consists of low scrubby hills of 'maquis', and it is here that the great majority of orchids are to be found, growing in the open patches between thickets of Cistus plants and boulders. The walking is not always easy, and strong footwear is necessary, but the orchid lover should be amply rewarded for the effort involved. Ophrys species to look out for include *O. scolopax, O. speculum, O. sphegodes*, the beautiful *O. fusca var. iricolor* and *O. fuciflora forma maxima*. Orchis species will include *O. provincialis, O. pauciflora,* and *O. quadripunctata,* the latter often growing in profusion. *Serapias parviflora* is sometimes abundant, and both *S. lingua* and *S. cordigera* can be looked for. Mount Youktas near Archances in Crete provides a classic example of this type of habitat, as also does the area surrounding the fort at Nauplia in Argolis on the mainland.

Mountain areas are, generally speaking, more sparsely populated with orchids, although some species are peculiar to them. The higher areas are often very exposed, with the result that specimens are small and stunted. In sheltered areas, however, a fair number of the prevailing species may be found. Notable amongst these is the alpine *Cypripedium calceolus*, a rarity anywhere, but particularly so in Greece.

In the Field

An experienced plant-hunter covers a given piece of ground systematically. It is often found that where there are one or two different species present, there may very well be others, and for this reason it is usually more profitable to cover a promising area thoroughly, rather than to attempt to get through too much ground.

A slow steady walking pace is the ideal speed, and it is generally a mistake to look too far ahead, especially when searching for the smaller plants. With the latter, it is sometimes helpful to get down on the ground and search it at eye level, when small plants will be seen to stand out from the surrounding vegetation.

Equipment

Many people, on finding a plant, will want to record the discovery, and the ideal way to do this is by colour photography. Plants on slides or colour film retain their natural beauty, and can give great pleasure to other people. The most suitable type of camera to use is one of the makes of single lens reflex models at present on the market. It is not essential to go to great expense in the matter of accessories, but one necessity will be found to be one, or two, close-up lenses. These are not expensive, and are fairly easily attached to, and removed from, the main lens of the camera by means of a screw thread. A one-power and a two-power lens can be used individually, or combined to give a three-power magnification picture. It is a prudent safeguard to attach a plain 'skylight' lens to the main camera lens, and to keep it permanently in position. Should the camera be accidentally dropped, the main lens could well avoid damage. A small tripod and cable release may be found to be necessary in conditions of poor light, when an exposure of more than one eighth of a second is required, and a small pocket lens is useful when examining the floral parts of a plant.

Plant Photography

Those who are new to plant photography may find the following ideas helpful.

It will be appreciated that conditions in the field will not always be ideal for close-up flower photography. The light may be poor, or the best view of the plant facing away from the sun, necessitating a picture taken with the sun behind the subject. Generally speaking, the best results are obtained if a plant is taken with the sun shining from over the photographer's shoulder onto it, although with white subjects it is often better, if possible, to choose a moment when the sun is temporarily behind a cloud. It is important to get down near to the ground, so that the lens of the camera is as near as possible level with the centre of the flower spike. This avoids a foreshortened picture which makes for a limited area of sharpness, especially with a small subject. A slightly foreshortened view, looking down on the subject, can, however, be helpful where the sun is in front of it. Where a close-up lens is being used, the area of sharpness is small, and this should be taken into account when adjusting the aperture and exposure. A camera fitted with 'through the lens' metering will help in this respect.

Wind can often cause problems, but patience, and the use of as fast an exposure as possible, will reduce them to some extent. It should be remembered that the average person cannot hold a camera steady for exposures of longer than one-eighth of a second. If a longer exposure than this is necessary, it is advisable to mount the camera on a tripod and to use a cable release for the exposure.

Some photographers like to use an artificial background for their subjects, by placing a neutral-coloured board behind them. This practice often gives a better result photographically, but spoils what is probably a more artistic view of the plant in its natural surroundings.

Chapter IV

THE GENUS OPHRYS

The science of ecology, the study of a plant in relation to its habitat, plays an important part in the practical study of plants. It gives the field botanist information as to plant species likely to be encountered in any given type of countryside. Advance notice of this prior to a short visit can save time and avoid disappointment.

For the purpose of describing the orchids of Greece, it is perhaps convenient to divide their habitats into three main types; namely, type A, woodland, type B, open woods and olive groves and type C, open 'maquis' scrub.

OPHRYS APIFERA This beautiful downland plant, the British Bee orchid, never fails to delight the orchid lover each year it is found. Unfortunately, it is becoming steadily rarer in Britain.
Sepals pink, sometimes with a green median line down their length. Petals thin, shorter than sepals, brownish pink. Lip dark velvety brown, with a red basal patch and a dull white central marking, sometimes roughly in the shape of an 'H'. Appendix at extremity of lip turned inwards. (C)

OPHRYS ARGOLICA A rather variable species,

which often hybridises with others of the genus growing near it. It can be recognised by its somewhat rounded lip, and its central lip markings which often take the form of two adjacent circles resembling spectacles.

Sepals and petals pink, the latter about half the length of the former. Lip single-lobed, nearly circular in shape, its edges sometimes furry. Appendix turned inwards. (C)

OPHRYS BOMBYLIFLORA, the Bumble-bee orchid, is locally common, often being found in colonies. It is one of the earliest Ophrys to flower, sometimes being past its best when the majority of the others are in full flower.

Sepals and petals greenish brown, the latter short and blunt. Lip strongly three-lobed, the side lobes consisting of two prominent humps, the whole being velvety brown. (B and C)

OPHRYS CRETICA The Cretan Spider orchid is a distinct and beautiful species, occurring only on the islands of Crete, Naxos and Karpathos. The blackish lip with its white markings gives the plant a very striking appearance.

Sepals greenish, sometimes with a brown median line. Petals brown, shorter than sepals. Lip markedly three-lobed. Side lobes brownish purple, carried roughly at right angles to the middle lobe. Middle lobe almost black, with variable whitish markings, sometimes in the form of a central loop, with two parallel lines leading up to its base. (C)

OPHRYS FERRUM-EQUINUM, the Horseshoe

orchid, is another rather variable species which hybridises easily, making identification difficult. It gets its common name from its lip marking, which often takes the shape of a horseshoe.

Sepals and petals pink, sometimes whitish-pink, the latter approximately two-thirds of the length of the former. Lip large, velvet-brown, with a central marking in the shape of an inverted 'U', somewhat resembling a horseshoe. Outward turned appendix. (C)

OPHRYS FUCIFLORA The Late Spider orchid is a very rare British native, and one of the finest of the Ophrys. Similar in colour to the Bee orchid, it can be distinguished from the latter by its short, triangular petals, its larger, squarer lip, and its outward-turned lip appendix . Hybrids between the two species have been recorded. The *forma maxima* has especially fine flowers, and some beautiful examples of it are to be found in Crete.

Sepals and petals pink, the latter short, triangular or dagger-shaped. Lip large, rather square, with a prominent outward-turned appendix . Lip markings variable, sometimes in the form of an 'H'. (C)

OPHRYS FUSCA The type variety is one of the commonest of the Ophrys. A marked characteristic of the flower is its long, comparatively thin lip.

Type variety, *O. fusca var. fusca*. Sepals and petals green, the latter roughly two-thirds of the length of the former. Lip long, velvet brown, barely three-lobed, with two long, narrow grey-blue patches at its base. (B and C)

O. fusca var. iricolor has basal lip patches vivid blue. (B and C)

O. fusca var. omegaifera has a brown basal lip patch with a whitish mark in the shape of a 'W'. (B and C)

OPHRYS LUTEA This species is the commonest of the Ophrys, being abundant in some places. It is nearly always found growing in colonies.

Sepals and petals greenish. Top sepal curving forward over the column. Lip pointing forward parallel to the ground, brown basally, with a wide margin coloured bright yellow. (B and C)

O. lutea var. minor has two brown lines at the extremity of the lip forming an inverted 'V'. (B and C)

OPHRYS SCOLOPAX, the Woodcock orchid. There are a number of forms of this species in addition to the type. A marked characteristic of each form is the rather narrow and roughly oval lip, reflexed at its edges, with a prominent outward-turned appendix.

Type variety *O. scolopax var. scolopax*. Sepals and petals pink, the latter short and dagger-shaped. Lip velvet brown, reflexed and rather narrow with a short blunt 'horn' at each side of its base. Prominent outward-turned appendix. (C)

Ophrys scolopax var. attica. Similar in shape, but sepals and petals green. (B and C)

Ophrys scolopax var. cornuta. Sepals and petals pink, lip red-brown, often richly coloured. Basal 'horns' on lip long and sharply pointed. (B and C)

Ophrys scolopax var. heldreichii. Somewhat similar to *var. cornuta*, but sepals and petals often deeper pink and flowers often larger. 'Horns' at base of lip much shorter and blunter. Plant often opens one flower on spike at a time, this flower fading before the next one opens. (C)

II

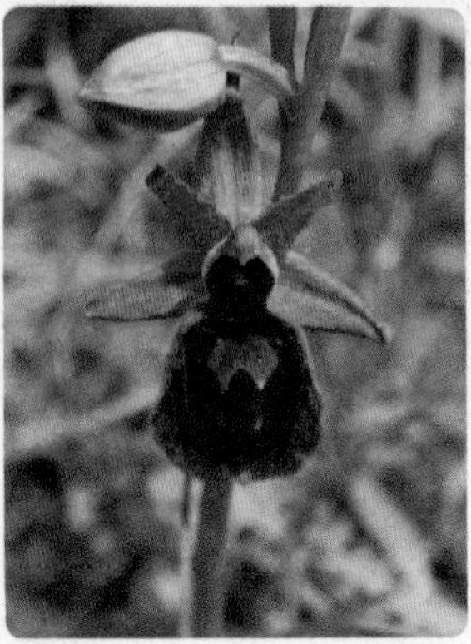
1

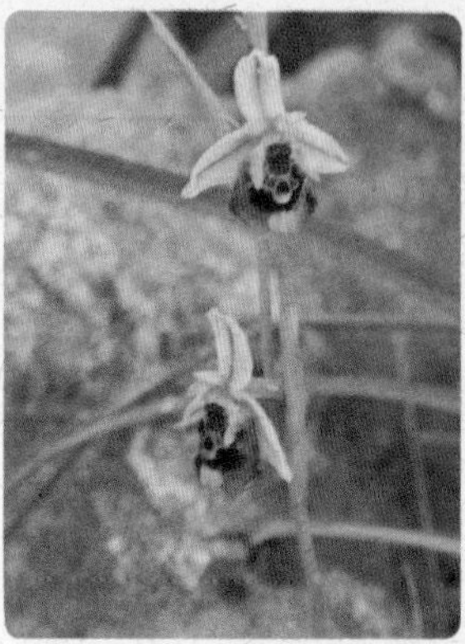
2

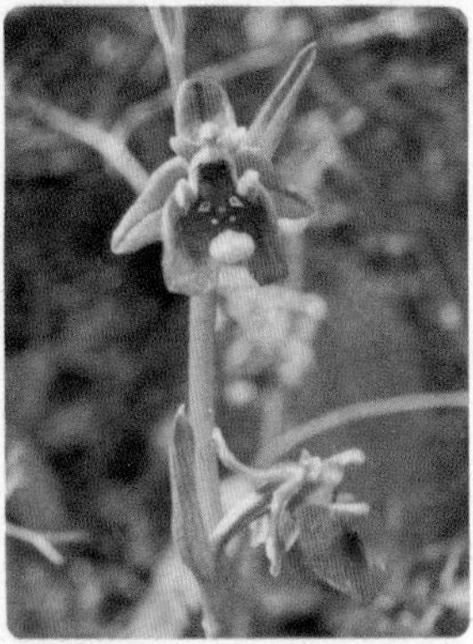
3

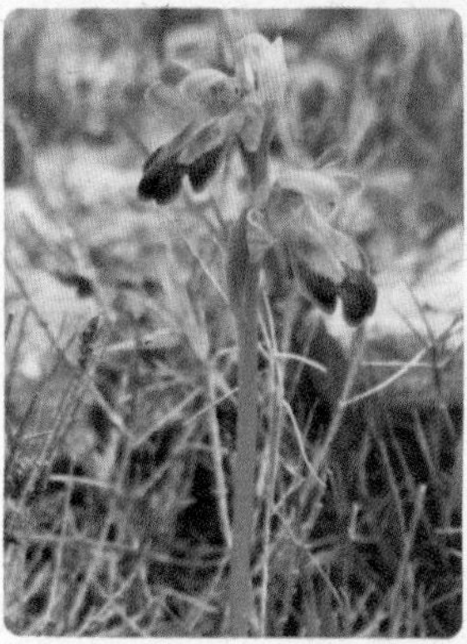
4

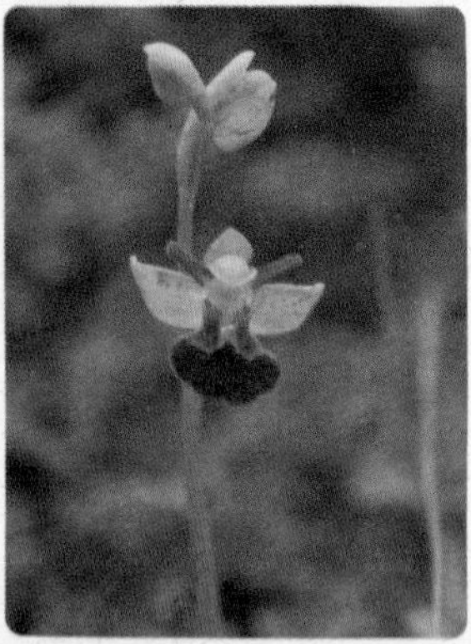
5

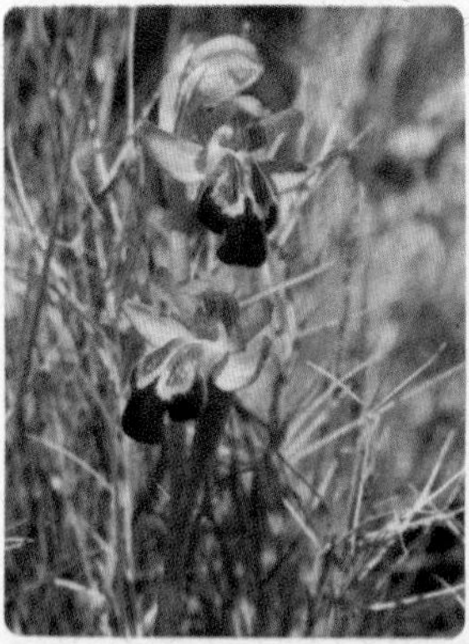
6

III

1

2

3

4

5

6

1

2

3

4

5

6

1

2

3

4

5

6

OPHRYS SPECULUM This beautiful plant, nick-named 'The Mirror of Venus' from the vivid blue patch on its lip, is often said to be the finest of the Mediterranean Ophrys. The colouring of its flowers makes it difficult to confuse with other species. Some very fine forms occur on the Greek mainland.

Sepals green, the top sepal invariably curved forward over the column. Petals dark brown, small and blunt. Lip three-lobed, side lobes yellow, edged brown. Larger central lobe edged with yellowish brown, the centre consisting of a large patch of vivid blue. All three lobes ringed with furry brown hairs. (C)

OPHRYS SPHEGODES The Early Spider orchid. The type variety is a British native. On the Continent the plant is very variable, and identification of the various forms is not simplified by the ease with which they hybridise amongst themselves.

Type variety *O. sphegodes var. sphegodes*. Sepals and petals green, the latter approximately two-thirds of the length of the former. Lip somewhat round, dark brown with a basal greyish blue marking often in the form of an 'H'. (B and C)

O. sphegodes var. spruneri. Sepals and petals pink, lip almost black with whitish line markings. Locally common. (B and C)

O. sphegodes var. mammosa. Comparatively rare. Sepals and petals deep pink, sometimes red, lip large and rather square, brownish black with two light brown parallel lines down its length. (B and C)

O. sphegodes var. aesculapii. Sepals and petals green. Lip brown, somewhat reflexed, with a broad yellow band round the edge. (B)

O. sphegodes var. litigiosa. Similar to *var. aesculapii*, but lip more reddish brown, and yellow band narrower. (B)

OPHRYS TENTHREDINIFERA The Sawfly orchid is one of the most striking of the Ophrys. A good form is a very handsome sight, with its colour combination of pink and yellow.
Sepals and short triangular petals pink, the top sepal often curving over the column. Lip large and flared, with a red-brown central patch and a broad edge of bright yellow. Outward-turned appendix . (B and C)

Chapter V

THE GENUS ORCHIS

The name 'orchis' has occasionally been used in the past when referring to plants which do not belong to the genus Orchis. Strictly speaking, the word 'orchid' can be defined as the name given to any plant which belongs to the family Orchidaceae, and the word 'orchis' as the name given to any plant which belongs to the genus Orchis within that family.

The flowers of Orchis differ from those of Ophrys in that they are smaller, and are carried in greater numbers clustered more densely on the flower spike. Broadly speaking, the floral structure is the same, with the addition of a long tube-like extension to the base of the lip, known as the spur, to which insects are attracted by the nectar within it. In Ophrys this organ is absent, the flowers relying on their powers of mimicry to attract insects.

ORCHIS ANATOLICA This is a slender plant, bearing small loose spikes of purple flowers. The long upturned spur is a noticeable feature. The plant is sometimes found in shady woods, but it also occurs in open scrub, where the spikes are mostly shorter and paler.

Sepals upright, petals curved forward clasping

column. Lip three-lobed, with long upturned spur. Base of lip white spotted purple, all other floral parts pinkish purple. (A and B)

ORCHIS CORIOPHORA, the Bug orchid, is rather local in Greece. It is commoner in the western Mediterranean region, where some fine specimens are to be found, notably in the Balearic Islands of Majorca and Minorca. The flowers are usually rusty red in colour, and are carried rather close to the stem. They have an unpleasant smell.

Sepals and petals brown or rusty red, the top sepal and petals forming a hood over the column. Lip three-lobed, the inward-turned middle lobe longer than the side lobes. Base of lip whitish, spotted brown. Downward pointing spur. (B and C)

ORCHIS CORIOPHORA VAR. FRAGRANS Flowers vanilla-scented and paler. Central lobe of lip longer. (B and C)

ORCHIS ITALICA The Italian Monkey orchid is one of the largest and finest of the genus. Some magnificent specimens occur in Crete. The flowers are an over-all deep pink, and the spikes sometimes attain a height of one foot or more, making the plants easy to see from a distance. *O. italica* is one of a group of plants whose flowers resemble a human figure. The lip is the most conspicuous part of the flower. Its two side lobes form the 'arms' of the figure, while the triple forked central lobe forms the two 'legs' and the 'tail'. The central part of the middle lobe represents the 'body' and the sepals and petals, which form a hood over the column, represents the 'head'. The over-all impression of each flower on the spike is that of a dancing figure.

Sepals and petals pink, striped with deeper pink, all curved over column. Lip long, three-lobed, pale pink spotted with deeper pink, spur short. (B and C)

ORCHIS LACTEA The Milky orchid is a short, rather thickset plant, seldom reaching more than six inches in height. The flowers roughly resemble a human figure, but the 'arms' and 'legs' are thick and blunt.

Sepals and petals whitish, striped longitudinally with green, and curved over column. Lip strongly three-lobed, side lobes thick, central lobe bluntly forked. Over-all lip colour milky white densely spotted with red. Downward pointing spur. (A and B)

ORCHIS LAXIFLORA The Jersey orchid is, as its name implies, a native of the Channel Islands, but it is absent from the British mainland. It is a tall plant, large specimens sometimes reaching two feet in height, and its rather deep purple flowers are borne on a loose spike. Some fine forms occur in Corfu.

Sepals reflexed, petals clasping column. Lip broad, sides reflexed, scarcely three-lobed. Long backward-pointing spur. Over-all colour deep purple, except for basal white lip patch. (B and C)

ORCHIS MASCULA The Early Purple orchid is a common British native, and is the earliest of the British orchids to flower. In late January its compact rosettes of purple-spotted shiny green leaves, from which the flower spikes rise to open in May, can be looked for in woods and hedgerows. In Greece it is uncommon, and is essentially a mountain plant. The

colour of the flowers varies, ranging from rare whites, through pink, to deep purple.
Sepals upright, petals clasped over column. Lip barely three-lobed, the sides reflexed, basally whitish spotted purple. Long upturned spur, somewhat flattened at its tip. (A)

ORCHIS MORIO. The Green-winged orchid, a locally common British native, takes its nickname from the green stripes on its lower sepals.
Leaves unspotted. Sepals and petals purple, lower sepals longitudinally striped green, all loosely clasped over column. Lip purple, white basally, three-lobed, side lobes reflexed. Upward pointing spur. (B)

ORCHIS PALLENS This attractive species flowers later than most Greek orchids, being at its best in May and June. The flower spike is rather dense, and the leaves unspotted.
Flowers butter yellow. Top sepal and petals curved over column, lower sepals free. Lip somewhat round, three-lobed, the central lobe smaller than the side lobes. Downward pointing spur. (A)

ORCHIS PAPILIONACEA The European Butterfly orchid is often rather local in Greece, but where it occurs it is sometimes numerous. Its colour combination of red and pink makes it quite conspicuous, and a large flowered form is a fine sight.
Sepals upright, red or deep pink. Petals clasping column, paler, striped with red. Lip large and flared, single-lobed, pale pink striped with pinkish red. Downward pointing spur. (B and C)

ORCHIS PAUCIFLORA This species and the following one are somewhat similar, *O. pauciflora* being regarded by some authorities as a variety of *O. provincialis*. The distinguishing features lie in the shorter, fewer flowered spike of *O. pauciflora*, its normally deeper colour, its smaller flowers and its more strongly reflexed lip.

Sepals and petals yellow, the former upright, the latter clasping column. Lip rather narrow, strongly reflexed at its sides, deep yellow, often basally spotted with red. Long upturned spur. (B and C)

ORCHIS PROVINCIALIS The Provence orchid is a tall stately plant, normally bearing a loose spike of pale yellow flowers; the flower colour can, however, range from deep yellow to almost white.

Sepals free, petals clasping column. Lip bluntly three-lobed, the central lobe forked. Spur long and flat, curving upwards. (B)

ORCHIS QUADRIPUNCTATA The Four-spotted orchid is a pretty little plant, locally abundant in Greece. It seldom reaches more than six inches in height, and its small purple-lilac flowers are rather flat.

Sepals upright, petals clasping column. Lip flat, three-lobed, the middle lobe square tipped. Base of lip whitish, carrying four purple spots arranged roughly in a square. All other floral parts lilac-purple. Long downward-pointing spur. (B and C)

ORCHIS SACCATA This plant is also known as *O. collina*. It is one of the largest flowered and most distinctive of the genus, and its colour combination is unusual.

Sepals upright, reddish brown, sometimes shaded with green. Petals pink, clasping column. Lip single-lobed, spreading, barely reflexed at its sides, deep pink with white basal patch. Short, blunt, downward-pointing spur. (B and C)

ORCHIS SIMIA The Monkey orchid is a very rare British native. It can sometimes be confused with *O. italica* where they occur together in the field, and in fact hybrids between the two are by no means unknown. Generally similar in shape to *O. italica*, *O. simia* differs in having thinner, less flat, 'arms' and 'legs', and in its habit of opening its flowers from the top of the spike, rather than from the bottom in the usual way.

Sepals and petals whitish pink, all curved forward in a hood over column. Lip whitish, similar in shape to that of *O. italica*. 'Arms', 'legs' and 'tail' often curled at their extremities and usually red-purple in colour. Red spots on 'body'. Short downward-pointing spur. (B and C)

ORCHIS TRIDENTATA O. lactea is treated by some authorities as a variety of this species. The flowers of the two plants are somewhat similar in shape, while those of *O. tridentata* are normally pink, and are clustered more densely on the stem. The flower roughly resembles a human figure.

Sepals and petals pink, forming a hood over column. Lip strongly three-lobed, middle lobe bluntly forked at its extremity. Colour of lip white, heavily spotted with pink. Long downward-pointing spur. (B and C)

Chapter VI

SERAPIAS AND OTHER GENERA

SERAPIAS

The plants of this genus, commonly called Tongue orchids, produce flowers which cannot be mistaken for those of any other. Identification of species within the genus is, however, a different matter. Classification is often made very difficult, if not impossible, due to the ease with which some of the species inter-hybridise.

The flowers possess a remarkable structure. They are carried on the stem in much the same way as those of Ophrys, but here the similarity ends. A sheath-like bract is produced at the junction of each flower-stalk with the main stem, partially concealing the flower-stalk itself. The lip is the most prominent organ. It is three-lobed, its two side lobes curving upwards over the column. The central lobe gives the plants their nickname. It curves forwards and downwards, and is often tongue-shaped. In some species it is covered with fine hairs. The sepals and petals form a helmet-shaped hood over the upturned side lobes of the lip.

Many of the species are found in dry, stony places, and plants of different species often occur in mixed colonies, hence the ease with which they inter-hybridise.

41

SERAPIAS CORDIGERA The Heart-shaped Serapias is one of the finest of the genus. The predominant feature of its flower is the big, heart-shaped lip, which is usually rich red-brown in colour.

Plant sturdy, stem spotted at base. Bract and hood fairly short, greyish purple. Lip rich red-brown, sometimes wine-red, often furry. (B and C)

SERAPIAS LINGUA This is a slender plant, bearing a rather loose spike. It can often be recognised by the middle lobe of the lip, which is usually carried at right angles to the side lobes, perpendicular to the ground. *S. lingua* is a common plant, with a wide range of distribution in Europe.

Bract pink, hood pink to brown. Colour of lip very variable, pinky-red, brown or yellowish. Central lobe often perpendicular to the ground. (B and C)

SERAPIAS NEGLECTA VAR. IONICA The type variety of this beautiful orchid does not occur in Greece, but the species is represented by its variety ionica from Corfu. A marked feature of the plant is its rather open lip, which appears more obviously three-lobed than in other species. It possesses a hump in the 'throat' at its base.

Plant less sturdy than *S. cordigera*, stem unspotted at its base. Bract and hood short, pink, the latter striped with reddish pink. Lip long, roughly perpendicular to the ground, its side lobes prominent. (B)

SERAPIAS ORIENTALIS The Eastern Serapias is a rather local plant, somewhat similar to *S. neglecta var. ionica* in the shape of its flowers, although the lip does not appear to be so obviously three-lobed.

Bract and hood short, lip fairly broad, rather oval in shape with two red humps at its base. Flowers pinky brown in colour. (B and C)

SERAPIAS PARVIFLORA The small-flowered Serapias is a common species, often found growing in colonies. It can be distinguished by its lip, the central lobe of which is bent sharply back, parallel with the flower-stalk. A yellow-flowered form is known, and the author has seen a white-flowered form in Corfu.
Flowers very small. Bract greyish-purple. Hood long, virtually covering side lobes of lip. Lip brick-red, the central lobe narrow and pointed, bent backwards parallel with the flower-stalk. (B and C)

SERAPIAS VOMERACEA (Syn. *S. pseudo-cordigera*) This is a rather variable species, but it can often be identified by its very long pointed bract, and by its thin lip which tapers to a sharp point.
Bract and hood very long, sharply pointed, greyish brown, the hood brownish red on the inside. Lip deep red-brown, long, thin and sharply pointed. (B and C)

OTHER GENERA

ACERAS ANTHROPOPHORUM The Man orchid is a British native, occurring mainly in south-east Britain. On the Continent it is more widespread. The flowers closely resemble a human figure, their general design being similar to that of *Orchis simia*, save for the absence of a 'tail'. There is no spur.
Sepals and petals forming hood over column. Lip three-lobed, middle lobe very thin, deeply forked at its

extremity. All floral parts yellowish-brown, in some forms reddish-brown. (B and C)

ANACAMPTIS PYRAMIDALIS The Pyramidal orchid is a locally common British native. It can be distinguished by its densely clustered pyramid of deep purple flowers, borne on a rather slender stem.
Top sepal and petals clasping column, lower sepals free. Lip markedly three-lobed, each lobe somewhat square-tipped. Long downward-pointing spur. All floral parts deep purple. (B and C)

   A. pyramidalis var. brachystachys often replaces the type variety in Greece. It differs from it only in its pale pink flowers.

BARLIA ROBERTIANA (Syn. *Himantoglossum longibracteatum*) The Giant orchid is one of the largest and finest of the Mediterranean orchids. The author has seen a Cretan plant which measured one foot five inches in height, carrying some sixty flowers. Each flower roughly resembles a human figure. The colour of the spikes varies according to the situation of the plant. Specimens growing in the open often fade to greyish-brown, while those growing in shady surroundings exhibit their natural colour combination of grey, purple and green. The large broad leaves are a prominent feature of the plant.
Top sepal and petals curved over column, lateral sepals free, dull greeny-brown spotted with purple. Lip three-lobed, central lobe purplish brown or olive green, whitish-grey at its base. Side lobes similarly coloured. Short blunt spur. (A, B and C)

CEPHALANTHERA CUCULLATA The species

comprising the genus Cephalanthera are essentially woodland plants, preferring beechwoods. In Greece they flower during May and June, later than most Greek orchids. They share the common name of Helleborine with their relatives the Epipactis, but they differ from that genus in not fully opening their flowers. *C. cucullata* is a rare plant, occurring in Crete.

Leaves very short. Sepals, petals and lip pink or pinky-white. Green bracts at junction of flower stalk with stem. (A)

CEPHALANTHERA DAMASONIUM The large White Helleborine is locally common in Britain. The plants seem to be more tolerant of sunlight than others of the genus, sometimes occurring at the margins of woods, in semi-shade.

Leaves produced at intervals on stem. Flowers short-stalked, appearing from the leaf-axils and remaining only half open. Sepals and petals white, lip basally yellow, white at the tip. (A)

CEPHALANTHERA LONGIFOLIA (Syn. *C. ensifolia*). The Sword-leaved Helleborine is also a British native, but is much less common than *C. damasonium*. Its flowers are somewhat similar to those of that species, but they differ in being borne on a loose spike which rises above the long sword-shaped leaves.

Flowers similar to those of *C. damasonium*, but when mature open less than those of that species. Lip yellow at its extremity. (A)

CEPHALANTHERA RUBRA The Red Helleborine is a very rare British native. It is a slender plant, bearing its flowers from the junction of a short green bract with the main stem. The flowers open further than others of the genus.

Sepals and petals deep pink, lip basally yellow, otherwise deep pink. (A)

CYPRIPEDIUM CALCEOLUS Lady's Slipper. This beautiful orchid, a British native, has suffered much at the hands of plant collectors, and as a result it is on the verge of extinction in Britain. On the Continent too, its numbers are causing concern to conservationists. In Greece it is confined to mountainous areas in the north of the mainland, where it is a rare plant.

The flowers of Cypripedium differ from those of nearly all other orchids in possessing two separated anthers rather than two anthers combined in the column. The two lower sepals are joined. In the centre of the flower an organ known as the staminode covers the column, and on each side of the column behind the staminode, are the two anthers with the stigmatic surface between them.

The most notable feature of the flower of *C. calceolus* is its yellow pouch-shaped lip.

Leaves large and prominently veined. Flowers one, more rarely two, exceptionally three to a plant. Sepals and petals chocolate brown, the later twisted to form a spiral. Lip large, yellow, oval in shape, slightly ribbed at its extremity. (A)

EPIPACTIS ATRORUBENS The Dark Red Helleborine, a British native, belongs to a group of orchids with large, broad leaves carried alternately on the stem and surmounted by a rather loose spike of flowers. They are nearly all woodland plants, preferring fairly dense shade.

   E. atrorubens, however, provides an exception, frequenting rocky areas and the edges of woods. The lip of Epipactis is unusual. It consists of an epichile, or extremity and a hypochile, or basal portion.
Leaves rather purple on their undersides. Flowers ranging from purple to brick-red in colour. Hypochile rather darker than epichile. (A)

EPIPACTIS HELLEBORINE (Syn. *E. latifolia*) This is one of the commonest of the Epipactis, being locally plentiful in Britain. The flowers are normally borne facing one direction on the spike, and not from all round it.
Leaves very broad, spike usually many-flowered. Flowers variable. Sepals green, petals pink. Inside of hypochile red, outside pink or green. Tip of epichile curved upwards to form a tiny pouch, pink in colour. (A)

EPIPACTIS MICROPHYLLA This rare species can be distinguished by its very small leaves, which are little more than bracts clasping the stem. The flowers are often pendulous.
Sepals green, petals pinkish green, lip hypochile brownish red, epichile pinkish. (A)

EPIPACTIS PALUSTRIS The Marsh Helleborine, as its name implies, differs from others of the genus in frequenting damp marshy places. It is an attractive plant, smaller than the other species, and in Britain it is locally common. Sand-dunes are a favourite habitat.
Plant relatively small. Flowers variable, ranging from almost white to reddish brown. Sepals and petals

brown, the latter somewhat paler than the former. Hypochile of lip noticeably more open, white striped with reddish-brown. Epichile white, somewhat frilled. (B)

GYMNADENIA CONOPSEA The Fragrant orchid, locally common in Britain, is much rarer in Greece, favouring mountain country. It can often be recognised by its rather loose spike of flowers, which resemble those of Orchis in shape. It flowers during May and June.

Flowers fragrant. Top sepal and petals clasping column, lower sepals free. Lip bluntly three-lobed. Long downward-pointing spur. Over-all colour of flowers pink. (A and B)

HIMANTOGLOSSUM HIRCINUM VAR. CAPRINUM The British Lizard orchid, *H. hircinum*, is represented in Greece by this rather uncommon variety. It flowers during May and June. The flowers of Himantoglossum are very striking, the lip being the predominant feature. It is three-lobed, the central lobe being very long, reaching a length of perhaps one inch, and often twisted into a spiral. In the flower bud it is coiled up in much the same way as a watch-spring. The variety caprinum bears a looser spike than the type, and the flowers are less robust.

Sepals and petals green, clasping column. Lip pink, three-lobed, side lobes small, central lobe very long, thin and ribbon-like. Short downward-pointing spur. (A and B)

LIMODORUM ABORTIVUM This strange and rather beautiful plant contains no green colour pigment, and is unable to manufacture food in the same way as other plants. Instead, it obtains its nourishment from dead matter in the soil around it. Plants which live in this way are known as saprophytes, and should not be confused with parasites, plants which live on live matter.

L. abortivum may be looked for in rather open pine or oak scrub. Its bluish-lilac flowers and its saprophytic growth distinguish it from other species. Unfortunately, it sometimes develops the habit of opening only one flower on the stem at a time, and the top buds are prone to wither before they open.

Sepals and petals both clear of column, the top sepal somewhat hooded. Petals roughly two-thirds length of sepals. Lip single-lobed, tongue-shaped and pointed at its tip. All floral parts bluish-lilac in colour, with the exception of a brownish downward-pointing spur. Leaves absent, but stem encased in brownish bracts. (A)

LISTERA OVATA The Common Twayblade is a widespread British native. It is an insignificant plant, its yellowish-green spikes often blending with the surrounding vegetation. In Greece, it may be looked for in mountainous country.

Flowers small, sepals and petals partially curved over column. Lip long and thin, deeply forked at its tip. Spur absent. All floral parts green to yellowish-green. (A)

NEOTINEA MACULATA This species is a native of the west coast of Ireland. It is a small slender plant, bearing a tight spike of pinky-beige flowers. In Greece, it prefers mountainous country. Owing to its size, it has

D

to be searched for carefully. With a magnifying glass, each flower on the spike can be seen roughly to resemble a human figure.

Flowers pinky-beige, densely clustered on stem. Sepals and petals forming hood over column. Lip three-lobed, central lobe forked at its tip. Downward-pointing spur. (A)

NEOTTIA NIDUS-AVIS, the Bird's-nest orchid, is a British native. Like *Limodorum abortivum*, it is a saprophyte, containing no green colour pigment. It is a plant of deep woodland shade, its yellowish-brown flower spikes often rising from a bare carpet of leaves. In Greece it is a rather uncommon plant, flowering in May and June.

Leaves absent. The flower spike often carries one or two flowers well below the main cluster on the stem. Sepals and petals curved loosely over column. Lip deeply forked. Over-all colour of flowers yellowish brown. (A)

PLATANTHERA BIFOLIA the Lesser Butterfly orchid. This species, not uncommon in Britain, is rare in Greece. The creamy white flowers are sweetly scented.

Top sepal and petals clasping column, lower sepals free. Lip single-lobed, thin and strap-shaped. Long downward-pointing spur. Anthers parallel. (B)

PLATANTHERA CHLORANTHA The Greater Butterfly orchid is essentially a woodland plant. In Britain it is less common than *P. bifolia*, and in Greece it is a rare plant. The flowers of the two species are somewhat similar, those of *P. chlorantha* tending to be larger. The difference between the two lies in the anthers holding the pollinia, which in *P. bifolia* are parallel, but which in *P. chlorantha* diverge from the top in an inverted 'V'.

Flowers white. Top sepal and petals clasping column, lower sepals free. Lip larger and more pointed than that of *P. bifolia*. Long downward-pointing spur. Anthers divergent. (A)

Chapter VII

CONSERVATION AND THE FUTURE

There can be few people who are not aware of the growing need for the protection of all wildlife throughout the world. Conservationists are becoming increasingly worried over the gradual exploitation of wild places and the consequent loss of their wildlife populations. It has even been forecast that if this trend were to continue unchecked, man's own survival would be threatened before long. In Greece and other countries on the Continent the problem is not, perhaps, quite so acute as it is in Britain, due partly to the geographical size of the latter. This fact, however, does not deny the need for conservation in all European countries.

A great deal of organised work has been and is being done on an international scale to save plants threatened with extinction, and it follows that a proportion of this work is concerned with orchids. The work can, however, be supplemented in a number of very valuable ways by ordinary people who share a common concern for orchid conservation. The first of these is the rather obvious one of refraining from picking flower spikes and uprooting plants. The picking of a single flower spike will not, it can be argued, affect the survival of a plant which is growing in abundance, although it is clear that if everyone who visited a popular site did so, numbers would soon decline. What is more important is to avoid picking when numbers are few, even if future identification is the reason for so doing. It is preferable either to take a colour photograph for record purposes or, better still, to ask an expert to come and examine the plant on site. In Britain, the various County Trusts for Nature Conservation will often help in this respect, as will County Recorders appointed by The Botanical Society of the British Isles.

There is an important scientific objection to the picking of flower spikes. A number of orchids flower only once in their lives, and then die. These plants, which are said to be monocarpic, are solely dependent for their perpetuation on the production of seed, clearly impossible if the flower spike is picked. Further research has yet to be carried out in connection with this phenomenon, but it appears that it varies not only within a given species, but within individual specimens in a colony of that species. Amongst British plants which seem to be most affected by it are the Bee, Butterfly, Fragrant, Frog and Musk orchids. All these plants, with the exception of the Bee, belong to the same sub-tribe within the family Orchidaceae. Where numbers in a colony are few in any one year, having been quite numerous in the previous year, it could well be that a high proportion of the colony are monocarpic plants, making it important to allow the survivors to set seed.

The uprooting of a wild orchid with a view to cultivation should never be attempted. It is almost certain that the plant will die, and here again the reason is a scientific one. All orchids live in association with a fungus, and in order for their seeds to germinate and grow, this fungus must be present in the soil. The chances of its being present in the plant's new environment, where there are probably no other orchids growing, are very remote indeed. Some years ago, the author transplanted a specimen of *Orchis mascula*, the Early Purple orchid, which was about to be destroyed by new tar being laid on the roadside where it was growing. The plant was moved a distance of some two hundred yards, and yet it failed to reappear the following season.

Nowadays, the picking and uprooting of wild orchids is strongly discouraged in many European countries, if it is not in fact illegal. In Britain, orchids are protected under the Conservation of Wild Creatures and Wild Plants Act 1975.

In Britain the use of agricultural insecticides is doing a great deal of harm to wild orchids, not necessarily by direct contact, but by destroying their pollinating agents. People who are interested can help to remedy the situation by hand pollination of rare species. This practice, while perhaps not yet necessary on the Continent, is becoming increasingly so in Britain, especially where the genus Ophrys is concerned. Here then is a very valuable way in which the amateur conservationist can help. The task itself is simple, and consists merely of lifting the pollen from the anther of one flower, that is to say, from the tip of the column, and transferring it to the stigmatic surface of another. A needle or a thin piece of wire makes a useful tool for this purpose. It is wise to avoid self-pollination of a flower, and to cross-pollinate, where possible, between different specimens in a colony. A pocket lens will be needed when dealing with the smaller flowers. The remaining needs are a steady hand and a knowledge of the parts of the orchid flower. The value of this work will be readily seen when it is realised that the average number of seeds per seed capsule, that is to say, per fertilised flower, produced by the British orchids lies somewhere between 500 and 10,000, although the vast majority do not survive.

Amateur botanists in Britain can be of great help as members of their County Trusts, by reporting rarities seen, and by giving warning of any projected development which might endanger a valuable habitat.

The field of education provides a vital method by which the rising generation can be made aware of the need for conservation. A great deal is already being done in this field, and plant-lovers in the teaching profession can give valuable support.

If future generations can be brought up both to respect and to conserve wild plants, then perhaps there may yet be an assured future for what is surely one of the loveliest of them, the orchid.

Bibliography

Darwin, Charles M.A. F.R.S. *The Various Contrivances by which Orchids are Fertilised by Insects*

Huxley, Anthony and Taylor, William *Flowers of Greece and the Aegean*

Polunin, Oleg and Huxley, Anthony *Flowers of the Mediterranean*

Summerhayes, V.S. *Wild Orchids of Britain*

Sundermann, Hans *Europäische und mediterrane Orchideen*

Turner-Ettlinger, D.M. *British and Irish Orchids*

Williams, John G, Williams, Andrew E. and Arlott, Norman *A Field Guide to the Orchids of Britain and Europe*

Index